Contents

A trip to the sea
Focus on: ea, ee as in *sea, bee* 3

Mr E's trees
Focus on: ee, **y** as in *bee, baby* 12

Happy!
Focus on: y as in *baby* 20

Phonemes: ch, sh, th, wh, ph, a_e, ai, ay, e_e, ea, ee, y *as e*

'Tricky' words: my, can't, does, love, here, are

About this book

These short stories are designed to give children blending and reading practice. They are decodable, which means the words in them only include letter shapes and sounds that the children have learned. The stories gradually introduce 'tricky' words, building on the learning in the Red Series.

The progression links directly to the teaching order in the Letterland teaching range. Each story begins with a title page that provides important information for children and teachers.

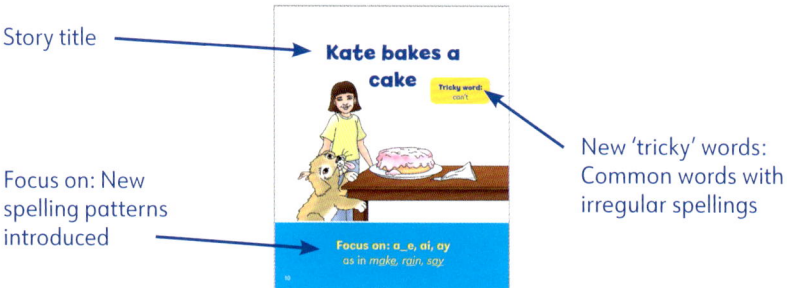

Story title

Focus on: New spelling patterns introduced

New 'tricky' words: Common words with irregular spellings

Basic teaching tips:

- Encourage the sounding out of decodable words (and any decodable parts of 'tricky' words).
- Discuss the stories with the children to ensure comprehension and engagement.
- Encourage re-reading in pairs or individually to develop fluency and reading for meaning.

Red Series introduces the a-z letters and sounds and some 'tricky words'. On completion of this series, the following words remain tricky in part: a, the, she, oh, for, that, ok, they, says, her, this, to, said, of, what, you, was, want, come, sees, asks, do. These words are included in **Blue Series**.

A trip to the sea

Focus on: ea as in *sea*

My Mum, Dad, Jean and I went to the beach. Dad said, "We can catch crabs. I can teach you."

Dad got a chunk of meat at the shop. "Yuck!" Jean said. "I will not eat that."

"The crabs think it's a treat," said Dad.

We went to the beach. The sea was cold. We screamed! From the rocks we spotted snails and fish.

"I can't see crabs," said Jean.

"The crabs will be in the seaweed," Dad said.

Dad gave us each a string. It had a bit of meat on the end. We put it in the sea. Then we waited.

"Tug it!" said Mum.

"I can see a crab!" I screamed.
I got the crab in a net, then I put it in a bucket.

Dad said it was a big crab.

Jean put her hand in the bucket. The crab reached to nip her. Jean named it, 'Nip'.

At the end of the day, we had a lot of crabs.

Dad said, "Do you want to eat them? "

Jean said, "No!"

"Let's just release them," I said.

Jean and I tipped the bucket. The crabs ran back to the sea. Nip waved at us as he ran off.

Mr E's trees

Tricky words:
here, are

Focus on: ee as in <u>bee</u>

This is Mr E..., and that is Mr E.
The Mr E's are twins, you see.

The twins are very keen on trees.
It's free to meet and greet the trees.

This green tree is the Greeting Tree.
It says, "Hello," to you and me.

Next we have the Buzzy Bee Tree.
The bees love it and we love bees.

Here we see a Squeezy Tree.
It hugs and squeezes Mr E.
Yes, the squeezes are for free.
It squeezes, then it yells, "Yippee!"

Here we see the Tee Hee Tree.
If you feel sad, just sit in this tree
and it will say, "Tee-hee, tee-hee!"
And then you will be filled with glee.

And here we have the Sweety Tree
with lots of sweets for you and me!
"Feel free to take the sweets," they say,
"but brush your teeth to stop decay!"

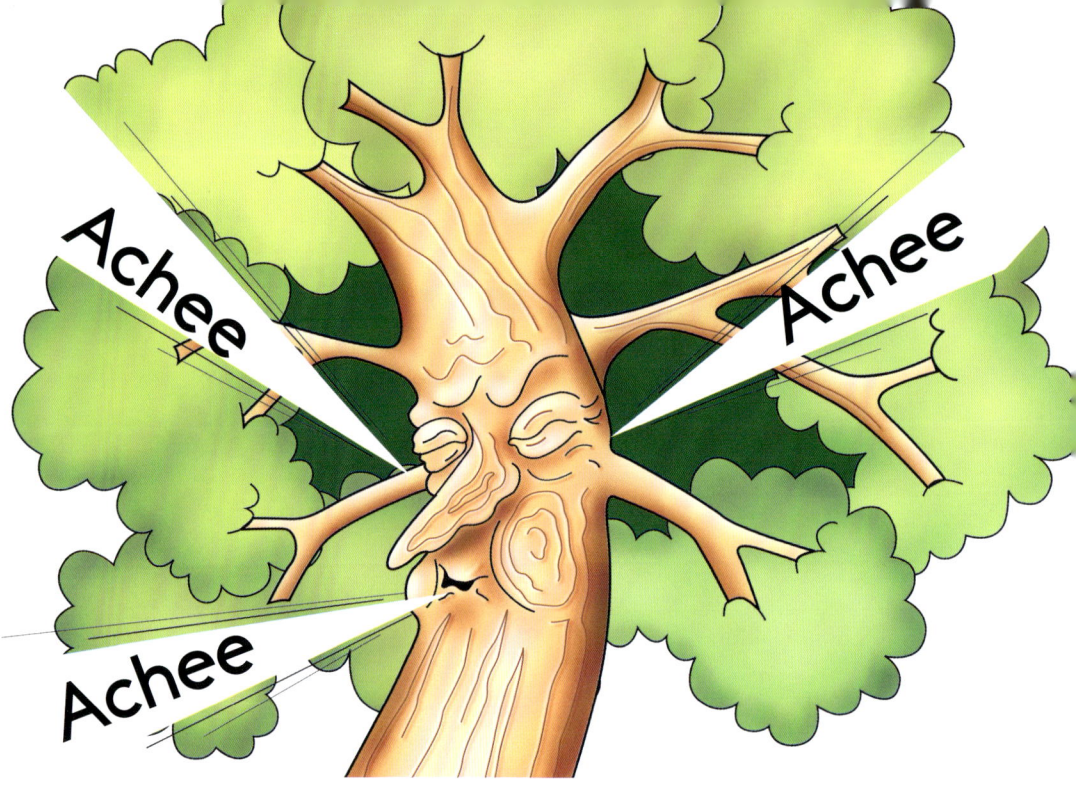

Have you seen this Sneezy Tree?
The sneezes seem to be in threes.
It sneezes, "Achee, achee, acheeee!"
So much so it makes a breeze!

At last we have the Sleepy Tree.
A twin sleeps here, as you can see.
Let's wake him with the Beepy Tree.
"Beep-beep, beep-beep, beep-beep!"

Happy!

Focus on: y as in *baby*

Ben is happy to be with the baby bunny. He gladly gives him a hug. The baby bunny is fluffy.

The puppy is happy to run with the pony. Run, puppy! Run, pony, run! The pony thinks it's funny!

About this series

This series of 10 books accompanies the Letterland teaching range. Each book contains a selection of short stories. In total there are 32 engaging stories featuring the phonic elements listed below as well as some 'tricky' high-frequency words.

Book	Focus elements	As in the word...	Story titles
1	sh, ch, th, th, wh, ph	chip, shop, that, thing	Check on the chicks Shep and me What is that thing?
2	a_e, ai, ay	make, rain, say,	A safe place Kate bakes a cake Kane's tail!
3	e_e, ea, ee, y	these, sea, bee, baby	A trip to the sea Mr E's trees Happy!
4	i_e, ie, igh, y	like, tie, night, my	Ben rides his bike Cats at night What a mess!
5	o_e, oa, ow	home, boat, show	The bad goat When the cold wind blows Lost in the Queen's maze
6	u_e, ue, oo, ew	cube, blue, moon, few, grew	Stuck on a dune A day at the zoo The Hat Man's new roof
7	ar, or, er, ir, ur, wr	farm, for, her, girl, fur, write	The big match Snapshots The bird girls My very bad morning
8	o, oo, u, oy, oi	son, book, put, boy, coin	Oscar's brother The big pull Nick's noisy new toy
9	aw, au, ow, ou	saw, cause, how, out,	Draw it! The house mouse Look now!
10	Review ear, air	pear, year, fair	My shark dream A fresh feast Bears at the fair A fairy story

Collect the sets

Phonics Readers - Red Series

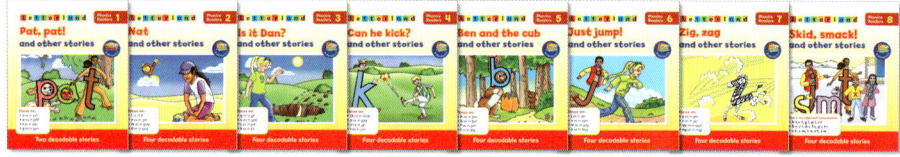

Phonics Readers - Blue Series

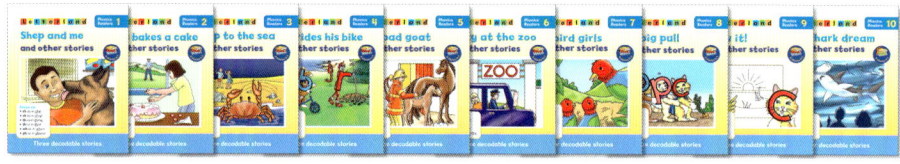

Published by Letterland International Ltd. 8/10 South Street, Epsom, Surrey, KT18 7PF, UK.
www.letterland.com
ISBN: 978-1-78248-182-9
Product Code: TJ04

© Letterland International 2016
LETTERLAND™ is a trademark of Letterland International Ltd.

First published 2013. This new edition published 2016.
Reprinted 2023.
10 9 8 7 6 5 4 3 2

Authors: Stamey Carter and Lisa Holt
Originator of Letterland: Lyn Wendon
Artwork: Doreen Shaw
Design: Lisa Holt

The author asserts the moral right to be identified as the author of this work. All rights reserved. No part of this publication may be reproduced, stored in a retrieval system, or transmitted in any form or by any means, electronic, mechanical, photocopying, recording or otherwise, without either the prior permission of the Publisher or a licence permitting restricted copying in the United Kingdom issued by the Copyright Licensing Agency Ltd, 90 Tottenham Court Road, London W1T 4LP. This book is sold subject to the condition that it shall not be way of trade or otherwise be lent, hired out or otherwise circulated without the Publisher's prior consent.

Printed in Beirut, Lebanon.